Scholastic Literacy Skills

Comprehension
Key Stage 2

Pupil's book

Editor   Clare Gallaher

Series designer   Joy White

Designer   Rachel Warner

Cover illustration   Joy White

Illustrations   Beverly Curl

Designed using Adobe Pagemaker
Processed by Scholastic Ltd, Leamington Spa

Published by Scholastic Ltd, Villiers House, Clarendon
Avenue, Leamington Spa, Warwickshire CV32 5PR

© 1998 Scholastic Ltd

3 4 5 6 7 8 9 0   9 0 1 2 3 4 5 6 7

British Library Cataloguing-in-Publication Data
A catalogue record for this book is available from the British Library.

ISBN 0-590-53889-6

Adapted from original material entitled 'Read Well' © Gordon Winch
and Gregory Blaxell published by Martin Education of Horwitz House,
55 Chandos St., St Leonards 2065, NSW, Australia

❀ Contents ❀

Unit 1

First day in Year 3

This is a **recount** of what happened during someone's first day in Year 3. A recount tells about an **experience** that happened in the past.

Before you read

- ❀ Write two things you remember about your first day in Year 3.
- ❀ Name two children or adults you remember clearly from your first day in Year 3.
- ❀ What was your happiest experience during your first day in Year 3?

Read this recount.

FIRST DAY IN YEAR 3

On Tuesday I went into Year 3. It was my first day in the Big School. Our class had some new children but most of them came up from Year 2. I knew them pretty well. I sat next to my friend, Ben. The new children had no friends. I felt sorry for them.

My new teacher was called Mr Rigg. He is quite young and really friendly. I found it hard to call him Mr Rigg. It was the first time I'd had a man teacher.

Our classroom looked a bit bare on the first day. There were so many things around the walls when we were in Year 2. Maybe all of last year's Year 3 had taken their work home. We will need to smarten our room up. I'll tell Mr Rigg. He won't mind.

The Big School was more strict than the Infants. Everyone seemed to be lining up all the time and you were not allowed to walk around the classroom much.

In the morning on our first day in Year 3, we did some writing. I wrote a story about our camping holiday. Ben didn't go away but he made up a story about a terrifying face-to-face meeting with a big snake. In his story he stared hard at the snake until it slithered away. In real life Ben would have run a mile! He's no hero, I can tell you.

In the afternoon Mr Rigg read us a great story about a haunted house. He made it sound really scary! I think I'm going to like Year 3.

Re-read the recount and answer the following questions.

1 What was the name of the writer's friend?

2 What was the name of the new teacher?

3 **a** What happened in the morning?
  b What happened in the afternoon?

4 What did Ben write about?

5 Why did the writer find it hard to call the teacher Mr Rigg?

6 Which classroom had more things around the walls, Year 2 or Year 3?

7 What things made the writer happy on the first day in Year 3?

8 What are the bad things about being new in a class or school?

9 Do you think the writer is a boy or a girl? Write your reasons for thinking so.

10 What does the writer mean by 'He's no hero, I can tell you'?

More things to do

Write a recount of your first day in Year 3, or your first day in any new school or class that you remember well.

Making scrambled eggs

A recipe is one form of **instruction**. It tells you **what you need** and gives you **step-by-step** instructions on how to prepare the dish.

Before you read

✿ Would you prepare scrambled eggs for breakfast, lunch or tea? Why?

✿ Who might you cook scrambled eggs for?

✿ What ingredients and kitchen tools might you use?

Read through this list of things you need and the steps for making scrambled eggs.

MAKING SCRAMBLED EGGS (SERVES 2)

Ingredients
4 fresh eggs
butter or margarine
milk
salt
parsley
bread

You will need
whisk or fork
mixing bowl
medium-sized saucepan
wooden spoon
chopping board
sharp kitchen knife
toaster

Making the dish
1 Break eggs into bowl and beat well.
2 Add small amount of milk and pinch of salt.
3 Beat again until well mixed.
4 Melt small amount of butter or margarine in pan.
5 Pour mixture into pan.
6 Cook until egg is not runny, stirring constantly with wooden spoon.
7 Chop parsley finely.
8 Toast and butter one or two slices of bread per person.
9 Spoon egg on to toast.
10 Sprinkle with parsley.

Re-read the recipe and answer the following questions.

1 How many eggs do you need for this recipe?

2 What would you use to beat the eggs?

3 What type of pan would you use?

4 What other method of cooking food is mentioned in the recipe?

5 Why do you think you use butter or margarine in the pan?

6 Why would you sprinkle parsley on the scrambled eggs?

7 How many eggs would you need to feed four people?

8 Scrambled eggs are often considered suitable food for young children or sometimes for people who are ill. Why might this be?

9 Name at least three other ways of cooking food.

10 Here is a set of commands for cleaning your teeth correctly. Write them down in the correct order.
Rinse out mouth and rinse toothbrush.
Squeeze toothpaste on to toothbrush.
Brush teeth up and down. Don't forget gums.

More things to do

Give a recipe for making toast with your favourite jam or spread. List the ingredients, what you need and the instructions.

Trouble at home

A **play** usually involves two or more characters talking to each other. This is called **dialogue**. A play often has some suggestions about where the scene is taking place and what the characters are doing. These are called **stage directions**.

Before you read

❀ From the title of the play, what do you expect it to be about?

❀ Write down the name of any play you have seen, heard or read.

❀ Are some radio and television commercials short plays?

Read this play.

TROUBLE AT HOME

Joshua is talking to Luke. They are on the school bus on their way home. Joshua is a bit worried because his dad has just lost his job.

JOSHUA: I don't know what Dad's goin' to do. He's lost his job.

LUKE: How?

JOSHUA: Company went broke.

LUKE: Went broke? So they let him go?

JOSHUA: Yeah. I don't think it's fair.

LUKE: What did he do?

JOSHUA: Drove a truck.

LUKE: That's bad luck! What's he goin' to do?

JOSHUA: Look for a job. He checks the paper every mornin'.

LUKE: Hasn't found anything?

JOSHUA: Naw! Rung up for a couple of jobs but didn't get 'em. *(He pauses as if he is thinking of something. He frowns.)* He gets grumpy about it.

LUKE: That's what happened to my dad. When he lost his job, him and mum started fightin'.

JOSHUA: Yeah I know!

LUKE: He went for a job today. A mate of his told him about it. I've got my fingers crossed.

JOSHUA: I hope my dad finds a job soon.

LUKE: Yeah, it's rotten. Got to get off next stop. Hope your dad finds somethin' soon.

JOSHUA: Me too. See ya.

Re-read the play and answer these questions.

1 Who are the two characters in the play?

2 Whose father has just lost his job?

3 What does Joshua's father now do every morning?

4 Where is Luke's father going today?

5 How do you know that Joshua is feeling worried?

6 At what time of day is the conversation between Joshua and Luke taking place?

7 Why do you think the play is called 'Trouble at home'?

8 What does 'Company went broke' mean?

9 What problems might be caused for a family if a parent lost his or her job?

10 How do people go about looking for new jobs?

11 What do you notice about this play that makes it different from an ordinary story?

More things to do

Choose a topic and discuss it with a friend. Write down what each of you said. Look at the kind of language you used. Work out if you need to put some instructions at the beginning or at various points throughout the text of the play.

Unit 4

The Hare and the Tortoise

In a **play** the characters are given lines to say to each other (or to themselves). When characters talk to each other this is called **dialogue**. Plays are usually acted on a stage, and the place where the action happens is called the **scene**. Instructions on how the stage should look and what the actors should do are called **stage directions** (they are often in italic writing).

Before you read

❀ Have you heard this story before? Can you remember who won the race?

❀ Write down at least one way in which a play might be different from a story.

Read this play.

THE HARE AND THE TORTOISE

Hare is talking to Tortoise. He is boasting about how fast he can run. They are in a woodland setting with a winning post at the back.

HARE: You are the slowest thing I've ever seen, Tortoise. Anyone could beat you in a race.

TORTOISE: I am slow, Hare, but you shouldn't be so sure of beating me. I never give up.

HARE *(in a scornful tone):* Tortoise, you are so slow you couldn't beat time. *(Laughing at his own joke)* Ha, ha, ha, ha.

TORTOISE: I might be slow, Hare. I might be slow. But I can tell you, I'm steady.

HARE: You could never beat me, Tortoise. No one has ever beaten me. Ever!

TORTOISE *(in a slow and steady voice):* I... could... beat... you... Hare.

HARE: We'll see about that, old slow coach. I challenge you to a race.

TORTOISE: And I accept the challenge.

HARE: Ready, get set, go!

Hare runs so fast he is soon out of sight of Tortoise. He stops, scratches himself and yawns.

HARE *(to himself):* Ho, hum! This is so boring, I think I'll take a nap. Ho, hum! Zzzzzzzzzzz...

TORTOISE *(comes along behind and sees Hare sleeping):* Well, look at that! I've just passed Hare! And I can see the finishing line ahead!
HARE *(wakes suddenly):* What! Where am l? Oh dear! Oh the race! I've got to get to the finishing line!
TORTOISE *(crosses the line ahead of Hare):* Too late, boaster. I've won! Remember in future: slow and steady wins the race.
AUDIENCE *(cheering):* Hooray for Tortoise!

Re-read the play and answer the following questions.

1 Who are the two main characters?

2 What did Hare do that made him lose the race?

3 What message did Tortoise give Hare in the end?

4 What is one thing Hare said that showed he was boastful?

5 Who did the audience like better – Hare or Tortoise? Explain why.

6 Here are some words that describe the two characters in this play. These words are called adjectives. Write the headings 'Hare' and 'Tortoise' in your notebook. Then list each adjective under the correct heading.

steady   boastful   overconfident   scornful   fast   slow
patient   impatient   determined   persistent   wise   rude

7 If you were Hare, what would you have done?

8 Do you think Hare will remember Tortoise's advice?

9 Do you think 'slow and steady' is always enough to win races?

More things to do

Act out or read this play with a friend. The class could be the audience and join in at the end.

Football

A **report** is organised into two parts: a **statement** of what the report is about, and **facts** about the subject.

Before you read

✿ How popular a sport is football?

✿ Does each player have a special job in a football team? What position would you like to play?

✿ Why do you think so many people like football?

Read this report.

FOOTBALL

Football, or soccer, is one of the most popular games around the world. It is played on a field that has goalposts at either end. There is a net behind the goalposts. This net catches the ball when it goes into the goal. The leather ball is round and is inflated with air.

There are two teams of eleven players. A team scores a goal when one of its players kicks the football into the net. This would be easier if there were no goalkeeper or goalie. The goalie's job is to stop the ball going into the net. He is the only player who is allowed to touch the ball with his hands. All the others have to play it with their feet or their heads.

Every player in the team has a job to do. The striker's job is to score goals. The forward's job is to get the ball to the striker. The midfielders attack and defend. The full backs and the goalie also defend.

Football is played by boys and girls, men and women all over the world. It is an Olympic sport. The most famous soccer event in the world is the World Cup. When teams play, many millions of people watch the matches on television.

Re-read the report and answer the following questions.

1 What is another name for football?

2 Where is a net used in football?

3 Is football played by both girls and boys?

4 What is the most famous football event in the world?

5 Why is it difficult to score a goal?

6 Why is the goalkeeper the only person who can handle the ball?

7 Why do so many girls and boys enjoy playing football?

8 Why is football watched by more people on television than any other sport?

9 What does 'Olympic sport' mean?

10 This report uses special football language. Write down the meanings of these words or phrases.
inflated with air
net
goalkeeper
striker
defend

More things to do

Find out the names of all the players in your local football team (or another team of your choice).
Find out the names of two famous soccer clubs from other countries.

The Fox and the Crow

A **fable** is a story that has a **message** about how to behave. The story begins by telling you what is happening, and when and where it happens. This is followed by some events which lead up to one main event. This main event changes, and finishes, the story.

Before you read

❖ Choose from the words below the one that best describes how a fox behaves:

cheerful   honest

sneaky   bad-tempered

❖ What sort of noise do crows make? Choose the words that best describe their call:

tweet-tweet-tweet

screech-screech

ar-c-k ar-c-k ar-c-k

Read this fable.

THE FOX AND THE CROW

Once there was a crow who had just found a lovely piece of cheese. She picked it up and flew on to the branch of a nearby tree.

Just at that moment a fox walked by. He looked up and saw the crow sitting on the branch with the lovely piece of cheese in her mouth.

'I want that piece of cheese,' he said to himself, 'and I know how to get it!'

'Lovely morning,' he called out to the crow. 'How well you look this morning. I've never seen you looking more beautiful. Your eyes sparkle like the running stream. Your feathers are as black and as glossy as the river stones, and I know your voice is just as beautiful. Please crow, is there any chance that you might sing me a song on such a beautiful day as this?'

The crow listened. 'What a nice fox he is! Yes, I'll sing for him,' she thought. So she opened her mouth, but only a loud 'ar-c-k, ar-c-k' came out. It really was an awful sound.

As she opened her mouth to sing, she dropped the cheese on to the ground. Quick as a flash, the fox snapped it up and gobbled it down.

'That's all I wanted, crow. But I'll give you a piece of advice. Don't trust people who flatter you.' And with that he ran off into the undergrowth, still licking his lips.

Re-read the fable and answer the following questions.

1 What had the crow found on the ground?

2 Where did the crow fly to eat her piece of cheese?

3 How did the fox plan to get the piece of cheese?

4 What happened when the crow began to sing?

5 The story ends with the fox giving the crow some advice. Write down what that advice is.

6 Why did the fox think that his plan would work?

7 Why did the crow forget that if she opened her mouth, the cheese would drop out? What was she thinking about?

8 What other birds might sing better than crows?

9 Crow says, 'What a nice fox...' Do you think the fox really is nice?

More things to do

The change in the story comes when the crow opens up her mouth to sing. How might the story have ended if the crow had looked down at the fox and thought to herself, 'I know he's trying to trick me. I'll just fly away'? Try writing a new ending to the story.

This fable was written by a very famous Greek writer called Aesop. Read some more of his fables. Choose your favourite, and tell it to the class.

We should look after our trees

An **argument** gives a particular **view** about something and the information which supports this view. At the end it **sums up** all the points that have been made.

✿ What are two things you like about trees?

✿ Do you know the name of a type of tree that you see near your house or school?

✿ Write one reason why trees are important to birds and animals.

Read this argument.

WE SHOULD LOOK AFTER OUR TREES

We should always remember to look after our trees as they are very important for our planet and in our lives.

First, trees keep the air pure because they give off the gas oxygen, which humans and animals need to breathe. They also take in other gases that we do not need.

Second, because the roots of trees hold the soil together they stop it from being washed away. In some parts of the world where a great many trees have been cut down, the land has been completely destroyed.

Trees provide homes for many different types of birds and animals, and they also supply their food. If trees are cut down, there will be no place for these birds and animals to live and nothing for them to eat.

In addition, trees often help in keeping us cool because they shade us from the hot sun. Sometimes they also offer shelter or protection from bad weather.

Finally, trees are beautiful to look at. The world would be a much uglier place if there were no trees.

All around the world forests are being cut down. We should look after the trees that are left and make sure that more are planted to replace those that have already been destroyed.

Re-read the argument and answer the following questions.

1 Write a list of five reasons why we should look after our trees. Use your own words.

2 Why are trees important to animals and birds?

3 Why might trees be very important in summer?

4 What parts of trees do you think birds and animals eat?

5 What do you think is the main idea in this argument?

6 Write a sentence which sums up the argument.

7 Place the following sentences in the order in which they appear in the argument. Write them in your notebook.

Trees keep us cool because they shade us from the hot sun.

Trees are beautiful to look at.

Trees keep the air pure because they give off oxygen.

Trees provide homes for birds and animals.

The roots of trees hold the soil together.

8 Imagine a world without trees. Can you list some bad things about it?

9 What do you like most about trees?

10 What is your favourite tree? Why?

More things to do

Your friend has offered to give you a kitten. Write an argument to persuade your mum or dad that you should keep it.

Unit 8

Tug of war

An **instruction** tells you how something is done. Rules for games are instructions. These rules tell you **how many players** there are, **what you need** to play the game and the **steps** you must follow.

Before you read

❁ Write the name of your favourite game.

❁ Write one thing you need to have to play it.

❁ Write two things you have to do when you play it.

Read how to play this game.

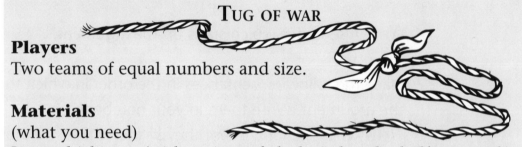

Tug of war

Players
Two teams of equal numbers and size.

Materials
(what you need)
Long, thick rope (with a piece of cloth tied at the halfway mark).
Line on the ground.

Steps
(what to do)
1 Line teams up facing each other.
2 Tell teams to hold rope.
3 Give order, 'Pull!'
4 Declare winner when one team pulls the other over line marked on the ground.

Re-read the instructions and answer the following questions.

1 What do these instructions tell you about? Write your answer as a sentence.

2 Name two things you need for a tug of war.

3 How many players are needed to play the game?

4 How does a team know when to start?

5 What does a team need to do to win?

6 Why do you think the teams should be of equal number and size?

7 Why does the rope need to be thick?

8 What sort of people would you like to have on your team in a tug of war?

9 Have you ever run in a book race (where you race with a book on your head!)? Here are the steps for that race. Write them down in the correct order.
Tell runners who drop book to go back to start.
Begin race.
Give prize to runner who is first over line with book on head.
Line up runners, each with book on head.

10 Tug of war is a team game. Do you know what this means? Name two other team games.

More things to do

Think of a game you like to play. Write its name, followed by instructions on how to play it. You could use the instructions for 'Tug of war' to help you.

King Midas and the golden touch

A **myth** is an old story (a **narrative**) which tells of gods, heroes, imaginary men and women from the past and magical happenings. Many myths come from ancient cultures – this one is a Greek myth.

Before you read

✿ Hercules was a hero from Greek myths. What do you know about him?

✿ Jason was another Greek hero. Do you know the name of his ship, his travelling companions and the treasure they were seeking?

Read this myth.

KING MIDAS AND THE GOLDEN TOUCH

There once lived a king called Midas. He was very greedy and believed that the most important thing in the world was gold.

'If only...' he said to himself, 'if only I could turn things into gold, I would be the happiest man in the world.'

At that moment a beam of sunlight streamed into the room, and from it appeared a young man who said to the king, 'I grant your wish, King Midas. Everything you touch will turn to gold.'

Next morning, when King Midas awoke, he found he already had the golden touch. The chair beside his bed turned to gold as soon as he touched it, the cover on the bed turned to gold, the curtains, a book on the table... Midas was overjoyed. At last he could have all the gold he wanted!

A servant arrived, carrying his breakfast. Midas decided to eat it right away. Imagine his surprise when the pancakes on the tray turned to gold when he touched them, the fresh fruit on the plate turned to gold, even the egg in the eggcup turned to gold!

'However will I eat?' Midas asked his beautiful, young daughter, Marigold, as she skipped into his room to wish him good morning. 'I will starve to death.'

Marigold ran to Midas and threw her arms around him. He bent down to kiss her. Alas! Her rosy cheeks were suddenly cold, hard and yellow. His daughter had turned to gold!

King Midas was overcome with grief. What had he done! Just at that moment the young man appeared again in a beam of sunlight.

'Have you learned anything, Midas?' he asked.

'Oh, yes,' replied the unhappy king. 'Gold does not bring true happiness. Take away the golden touch.'

The young man granted his wish, the golden touch left Midas and Marigold came back to life. 'Ah!' said Midas to his daughter. 'The only true gold is the gold of your beautiful hair. I have learned my lesson.'

Re-read the myth and answer the following questions.

1 What was the name of the king? What was his daughter's name?

2 What was the first wish he was granted? What was the second?

3 How did Midas get his breakfast? What was he going to eat?

4 What was the first problem the golden touch brought to Midas?

5 What do you think was the worst thing that happened to him?

6 Midas didn't think ahead. How do you know that?

7 What clues are there that this story might be a myth?

8 What does 'I have learned my lesson' mean?

9 If you were granted a wish, what would you like most?

More things to do

Find out some more about Hercules and Jason.

Write what you would say if you were granted the 'golden touch' and why you would say this.

A lesson for young James

Poetry takes many forms. Many poems are quite short, but others tell a long story. The clues that show that a piece of writing is a poem are **line length**, **rhythm**, **rhyme** and **special words**. Sometimes all of these are used, sometimes just one or two.

Before you read

❀ What was the name of your first teacher at school?

❀ Is there anything special that you can remember about the person?

Read this poem.

A LESSON FOR YOUNG JAMES

Young James had always had his way
In nearly everything,
Until the day he went into
The class of Mrs King.

Now James was very spoiled, you see,
Before he started school,
But when he shouted out, 'I won't!'
His teacher lost her cool.

'You are at school now, little boy,
And you will quickly see
That saying "Won't" and "No" and "Yuk"
Just will not work with me.'

So James learned to behave in class,
He's quite a different boy.
And gets on well with everyone,
Which gives his teacher joy.

Gregory Blaxell

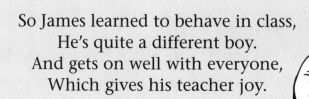

Re-read the poem and answer the following questions.

1 What was the name of James's first teacher?

2 What sort of boy was James when he first came to school?

3 Write down three words that James used a lot when he first came to school.

4 Why did James change?

5 What do you think the other children in the class thought of James when he first came to school?

6 What types of behaviour by your classmates do you particularly like or dislike?

7 What is meant by these phrases?
lost her cool
Just will not work with me

8 What do you remember about your first day at school?

9 What was the hardest thing about going to school for the first time?

More things to do

Write another verse for the poem about young James, or make up a poem about someone you remember from your first class in school.

Katy's dog

A **narrative** tells a story. It has a **beginning**, a **middle** and an **end**. At the beginning we meet the characters and find out when and where the story takes place. In the middle one or more things happen, then there is a crisis and at the end everything is worked out.

Before you read

❀ What are some good things about owning a dog?

❀ What are some things you have to consider if you plan to buy a dog?

Read this story.

KATY'S DOG

Katy's dog, Dylan, was her very best friend. He was a mixture of breeds and a mixture of colours. He had long legs, a short tail and long hair. He followed Katy everywhere and lay with his head on her foot when she did her homework. Katy loved him.

When Katy took Dylan for a walk on his lead he was very obedient and very gentle – unless Katy was in danger. Then he became a raging tornado.

One day Katy took Dylan to the park across the road. It was a big, open park but Katy's mum could watch them both from the kitchen window. She also knew that her daughter would be safe as long as her faithful dog was with her.

Katy threw a ball to Dylan and he ran and brought it back to her. They were having a great game when two strange dogs came into the park. They were big and fierce and ran towards Katy. Dylan dropped the ball and stood in their way. Unable to get to Katy they attacked Dylan instead. Dylan was a tough fighter and well able to stand up for himself. The noise frightened Katy, but she was able to run away, across the road to her mother.

Katy was safe, but what was happening to Dylan? Katy called to him.

'Dylan! Dylan! Here boy!'

There was no answering bark, no bounding dog ran to her. There were no dogs left in the park and everything was silent. Dylan had gone.

Katy looked for Dylan all the rest of the day. Her mum helped, and her dad when he came home. There was no sign of the lost dog. Something must be wrong.

'Maybe he chased the strange dogs and has got lost himself,' her father said. 'Dylan is bright, though. He'll find his way home.'

Katy did not sleep very well that night. She kept thinking of Dylan. Was he hurt? Would he ever come home?

Early in the morning she crept out of bed and went down to check outside the front door. Something muddy and rather battered was sitting on the mat. It wagged its stubby tail as Katy shrieked with delight.

Re-read the story and answer the following questions.

1 What was the name of Katy's dog?

2 What did the dog look like?

3 What happened in the park?

4 How did Katy's mother feel about Dylan?

5 What do you think usually happened when Katy called Dylan?

6 Do you think Katy's father was right in what he said about Dylan? In what ways was he right?

7 Why was Dylan muddy and battered?

8 What does 'he became a raging tornado' mean?

9 Describe how Katy felt at the end of the story.

10 Describe how you might feel if you had lost your pet.

More things to do

If Dylan could talk, what would he tell Katy when he came home?
Write your own narrative about a lost pet.

A letter to Grandma

Letters can do many different jobs. This letter is to a grandmother, telling her about a flight to the Channel Islands. It is a **recount**, so it starts off by giving her basic information on when and where. It then tells her more about the flight.

Before you read

❀ For what other reasons might you write to your grandma?

❀ Imagine that you are going to take a flight to the Channel Islands. What things might you think about during the flight?

❀ Why would you and your family go to the Channel Islands?

Read Stephanie's letter to her grandma.

Seaview Guest House
St Helier
Jersey

Wednesday

Dear Grandma,
   We caught the 10am flight to the Channel Islands on Sunday. It left Manchester on time and took just over an hour to get here.
   As we taxied to the end of the runway, the flight attendant told us a few things about the plane. She also showed us the exits.
   The pilot told us to make sure our seat-belts were fastened. Then he revved the engines and we began to race down the runway. It was great! The plane went faster and faster and I felt as if I was being pushed back into the seat. Then all of a sudden we were off the ground. Everything looked smaller and smaller as we went up.
   We went into a cloud and the plane started to bump. I closed my eyes. Dad and Mum closed their eyes too. I think they were a bit scared.
   We were given a sandwich and a biscuit, and I had a glass of lemonade. By the time the flight attendant had collected up the rubbish, the plane was coming in to land on Jersey. I could feel the plane descending in the sky and the pilot gave us a smooth landing. The engines make a lot of noise when a plane is landing!
   When we climbed out of the plane, it was much warmer. Then I knew we were really on our holiday.
   Mum and Dad send their love. Me too,

   Stephanie

Re-read the letter and answer the following questions.

1 From what part of the Channel Islands was the letter sent?

2 When did the flight leave Manchester? Was it morning or night?

3 Who told the passengers about the plane?

4 What did Stephanie drink during the flight?

5 What made the plane bump about?

6 Why did Stephanie think her parents were frightened?

7 Do you think Stephanie was a bit frightened too?

8 Do you think Stephanie had ever flown before?

9 Do you think she enjoyed the flight?

10 What do you think is meant by these words?
revved
descending

11 What do you think you would like most, or least, about taking a flight on a plane?

More things to do

Write a letter to your best friend telling him or her about last weekend when you and your family stayed at a caravan park right on the beach. Look at Stephanie's letter to see how she has written the address. Notice, too, how she finishes her letter.

Report

The fairy penguin

A **report** provides us with **facts** (information) about something. It begins with an opening **statement** and then gives us a number of different facts.

Before you read

❀ Do you think a penguin is a:

fish?

bird?

mammal?

❀ Which of these is true?

Penguins can fly.

Penguins can swim and walk.

Read this report.

THE FAIRY PENGUIN

Fairy penguins are the smallest type of penguin in the world. They live in the south of Australia and in New Zealand.

Fairy penguins weigh about one kilogram and stand 30 centimetres high. Their back feathers are dark blue and their front feathers are white. They have a beak, webbed feet and flippers.

Penguins live on the land and in the sea. They are very good swimmers and divers, but they cannot fly. They eat small fish and squid.

Fairy penguins breed on land. The female lays two white eggs in a burrow, and the male and female share the job of sitting on the eggs. When the babies hatch they are covered in white down.

At the start the mother and father bring food from the sea, but after eight weeks the baby penguins have grown feathers and are soon ready to hunt for their own food.

Fairy penguins are often in danger. They are hunted by wild animals; they are caught in nets and on long lines; if they get covered with oil, they drown. Many of their breeding grounds have been taken over by humans who have gone to live there. If their numbers become too small, these little penguins might disappear for ever.

Re-read the report and answer the following questions.

1 What are the smallest penguins in the world?

2 Where do they live?

3 What colour is the back of a fairy penguin?

4 What do fairy penguins eat?

5 Why would webbed feet be important for fairy penguins?

6 How do you think these penguins catch their food?

7 Why might an oil tanker sinking cause danger to fairy penguins?

8 Do you think that fairy penguins should be protected?

9 What do you think we should do to protect fairy penguins?

10 What do you think 'breeding grounds' are?

11 Complete these sentences. Write in your notebook.
Penguins _____ on the land and in the sea.
The females _____ two white eggs in a burrow.
They are soon ready to _____ for their own food.

More things to do

Here are some facts about bears. Write a report, using these facts.
Bears eat a wide range of food.
There are brown bears, black bears, polar bears, panda bears and others. Bears have thick fur coats.
Bears have sharp claws.
They do not see very well, but they have a good sense of smell.
Bears sleep during the winter.

A close shave

A **narrative** begins by telling the reader where and when the story is happening. It contains a series of events, leading up to one main event which changes the course of the story and brings it to an end.

Before you read

✿ What important things would you need to take if you went fishing in a boat?

✿ What are some of the dangers of fishing from a boat?

Read this story.

A CLOSE SHAVE

It was a clear morning. The sun was just coming up as we arrived at the slipway. There was hardly any breeze and it felt as if it could get very hot.

There were three of us going fishing – my dad, my best friend Hannah and myself. This was the first time Dad had taken us fishing from his boat.

We packed all the gear and Dad started the motor. Soon we were speeding down the river towards the sea. When we arrived at Dad's special spot, we put down the anchor and waited for the fish to bite.

In no time at all I felt a strong pull on my line. I reeled it in and saw I'd caught a nice mackerel. Dad helped me get it into the landing net. It made me feel pretty good that I'd caught the first fish. We caught three more fish after that.

It had become very hot and big, black clouds were starting to bank up. 'I think we'd better head for home,' said Dad. 'It looks like there's a big storm coming.' We wound up our lines and Dad asked me to pull up the anchor once he'd started the motor.

He pulled on the starter, but nothing happened. He tried again, and again. 'I'll just check the spark-plug,' he said. 'It can get a bit dirty.' He took out the spark-plug and looked at it. Just then, a big wave hit us. The spark-plug fell from Dad's hand into the water!

'I don't have a spare with me,' said Dad. 'And that storm is getting closer.' I could tell that he was angry with himself.

The sky had gone very dark and there was thunder and

lightning all around. Then, as I looked up, I saw a gust of wind coming across the bay. With it was a shower of rain.

'What'll we do, Dad?' I asked. I was scared. So was Hannah.

'Don't panic, you two. I've just remembered, Mum put the mobile phone in the bag. I'll ring the coastguard. They'll help us.'

And that's exactly what we did. In no time at all the coastguard launch arrived and they took us on board. Then they towed our boat back to the slipway. We were all really glad to get back on dry land because the storm had got a lot worse. We were all soaked through, but at least we were safe!

Re-read the story and answer the following questions.

1 How many people went fishing? Who were they?

2 Where did they put the boat into the water?

3 Where was the slipway located? A harbour, a lake or a river?

4 How many fish were caught all together?

5 What were the signs that a storm was coming?

6 Do you think that Dad was worried too? Why?

7 Why did they travel back in the coastguard launch?

8 What could have happened if they hadn't had the mobile phone?

9 How do you think the mother of the family felt, and what do you think she said when they got home?

10 What do you think the title of this story means?

More things to do

Draw a timeline showing the events of the day, beginning and ending at the slipway.

Why the sea is salty

An **explanation** makes clear **how** things work or **why** things happen. It opens with a **general statement** and then lists points which explain how or why.

Before you read

❧ Which is more salty, water from a tap or water in the sea?

❧ Where do rivers run to?

Read this explanation.

WHY THE SEA IS SALTY

The sea is salty because salt is washed into the sea from the land.

First, rain washes salt from the ground, and this salt dissolves in the rainwater before running into the rivers. When the rivers flow into the sea they carry the salt with them.

Every year millions of tonnes of salt are washed into the sea, and when water evaporates from the sea, the salt is left behind. This means that the sea contains more and more salt as the years go by.

The Red Sea and the Dead Sea are more salty than the oceans. This is because they have many rivers flowing into them. Also, they are inland seas and not very big, so the salt builds up. The extra salt in the water makes it very easy to swim in these seas.

The rain washes out the salt from the land

Salty water goes into the rivers

The rivers flow into the sea with the salt

Re-read the explanation and answer the following questions.

1 Does salt dissolve in water?

2 What carries the salt to the sea?

3 How much salt is washed into the sea each year?

4 Which seas are easy to swim in?

5 Is the Red Sea more salty than the Atlantic Ocean?

6 Will the sea become more salty as time goes by? Why?

7 What else do you think rivers carry to the sea besides salt?

8 Salt dissolves quickly in water. What else dissolves in water?

9 What do you think it would be like to swim in the Dead Sea?

10 Write these sentences in your notebook, marking them true or false.
When water evaporates from the sea, salt is left behind.
The oceans are more salty than the Red Sea or the Dead Sea.
Salt is carried into the sea by rivers that flow into the sea.

More things to do

In your notebook, write an explanation of why holidays are fun.
Write to a pen-pal who has never seen the sea, describing what it looks and smells like and how it feels to swim in it.

Going to school

An **argument** begins with the author stating a **point of view**. This is followed by **reasons** that support that point of view. The author ends by summing up and coming to a **conclusion**.

Before you read

✿ Why do you go to school? Give three reasons.

✿ What do you think is the most important thing you learn at school?

✿ Name some other places where you learn things.

Read through this argument.

GOING TO SCHOOL

Going to school is very important because during the years that we are at school we learn many things. By law, all children in the UK between the ages of five and sixteen must attend a school and be taught, or educated, in many subjects.

As very young children we learn to read and write. These are sometimes called literacy skills. We also learn to work with numbers (or numeracy). It is important to learn these skills. We need them for all kinds of things in life, as we grow up, not only for things we do at school.

At school we are also taught a great deal about our world and the people who live in it. By understanding other countries and other peoples we should be able to make our world a better place to live.

While we are at school we learn to work together and to help each other. This helps us to understand and appreciate what we can do best and also what others can do well.

Good health and fitness often begin with sports played at school which we enjoy, but which also help us to become fit and well. As being fit is important all our lives it is a good thing to recognise this at an early age.

At school we learn a lot of different things. Many of these will be of help to us all through our lives.

Re-read the argument and answer the following questions.

1 At what age must children in the UK start school?

2 For how many years must UK children attend school?

3 Name three things we learn about when we first go to school.

4 Complete the following, writing the sentences in your notebook.

   Reading and writing are sometimes called _____ skills.

   Another phrase for learning to work with numbers is _____.

5 Do we use these skills only while we are at school?

6 Why is it important to learn these things?

7 What does playing sport at school teach us?

8 How might we make our world a better place to live by knowing about other countries and the people who live in them?

9 What does the writer of this argument think is the most important thing we learn about at school?

10 What other things, not mentioned in the article, do you think are important lessons that are learned at school?

11 For what jobs, as adults, might we be glad of the numeracy skills we learn at school?

More things to do

Write an argument in which the main idea is one of your own choice.

Grasshoppers

Poems can be about many different things and come in many different shapes and sizes. Poems often use **rhyme**, a particular **beat** (or rhythm) and **special words**.

Before you read

❀ Are there creatures living in your garden or a park near your home that scare you? What are they?

❀ Are there creatures you would enjoy watching in a garden or park? Name three.

Read this poem.

GRASSHOPPERS

Do you hunt
Grasshoppers
In your backyard?
You do?
I do, too.

Do you keep
Creeping up
Till they hop?
Or do you stop?
You do?
I do, too.

Do you think
About catching one?
And holding it
Kicking
With its big back legs
In your hand?
You do?
I do, too.

Have you caught –
Really, truly
Caught –
A wild, green grasshopper,
Before it starts
To hop
Or fly?
No?
Neither have I.

Gordon Winch

Re-read the poem and answer the following questions.

1 What insect is the poem about?

2 What colour is the insect?

3 Does the poet rush after the insects or creep up on them?

4 Has the poet ever really caught one?

5 What helps grasshoppers jump so high?

6 Does any part of the poem make you think that the poet is a bit scared of grasshoppers? Which part?

7 The poem tells you a number of things about the poet. Copy out the words or phrases below that you think best describe him.

probably young   unafraid   brave   interested in creatures
probably old   afraid   timid   not interested in creatures

8 This poem is really about two things: grasshoppers and the poet.
a What does the poem tell you about grasshoppers?
b What does the poem tell you about the poet?

9 **a** In what ways are you like the person in the poem?
b In what ways are you different?

More things to do

Choose another insect or animal and write your own version of this poem. Start your poem like this:

Do you hunt _____ In your backyard?
You could choose from beetles, pigeons, tadpoles, frogs, butterflies or snails. Change the poem to suit the creature (tadpoles don't hop!).

Narrative

Catherine and the Carrot King

A **narrative** tells a story. It has a **beginning** (introduction), a **middle** (complication or crisis) and an **end** (resolution). In the beginning, we meet the characters and find out when and where the story takes place. Then a number of things happen – these events lead to a crisis and an ending in which everything is worked out.

Before you read

❀ Do you like carrots? What do you like or dislike about them?

❀ This story is a fantasy. (It couldn't really happen.) Write the name of a fantasy you have read or seen on television or at the cinema.

Read this story.

CATHERINE AND THE CARROT KING

'Not carrots again!' sighed Catherine. 'Mum gave me raw carrots for lunch as well. They took ages to chew and I didn't get any playtime. I hate carrots!'

Zing! Zap! Suddenly there was a flash like lightning and standing in front of Catherine was a fearful figure. He had a carrot-coloured cloak, a carrot-coloured suit, pointed carrot-coloured shoes and – believe it or not – a crown made of carrots on his head.

'I,' said the terrifying creature, 'am the Carrot King, feared ruler of Carrot Kingdom. My task is to teach children who don't like carrots just how good they are for them. You are my prisoner. Jump into the carrotmobile with the others. Quickly now!'

When the carrotmobile arrived at the palace of the Carrot King, the children were led into a carrot-coloured room through a carrot-coloured door. In front of them was a long table covered with dishes of carrots.

There were long carrots, short carrots, thin carrots, thick carrots, boiled carrots, baked carrots, steamed carrots, and – of course – raw carrots.

'This,' said the Carrot King, looking very fierce and peering at each child, 'is your task. You must eat every carrot on this table before midday. Leave one tiny piece and you will have me to deal with! Ready, steady, eat!'

Re-read the story and answer the following questions.

1 Did Catherine like carrots? What were her reasons?

2 What did the Carrot King look like?

3 What was on the table in the Carrot King's palace?

4 What task did the Carrot King set?

5 Who do you think were the 'others' in the carrotmobile?

6 Why do you think the Carrot King wants to persuade them to like carrots?

7 This story has two main characters. What are their names?

8 What things in the story show you that it is a fantasy?

9 If there were a Carrot Queen in this story how might she be dressed?

10 Finish the story. Think about what might happen, then draft your ending on a sheet of scrap paper. Write the final copy in your notebook. Use the following questions to get you started:
What will Catherine and the others do?
What will happen to them?
Will they finish all the carrots?
What will the Carrot King say and do when he returns?

More things to do

Read your ending to this story to a friend or to the whole class. Then listen to other children's story endings.

Unit 19

Learning to swim

A **factual report** begins with a **statement** of what the report is about and then gives some **facts** about the subject.

Before you read

✿ Can you swim? How did you learn? Write down the names of any people who taught you how to swim.

✿ Which of these did you find hardest when you were learning to swim? Write out your choice in your notebook.

Putting your head under water.

Learning to kick your legs.

Learning to move your arms and kick your legs at the same time.

Read this report.

LEARNING TO SWIM

Many children learn to swim when they are quite young. Sometimes they learn during the school holidays at special classes held at local swimming pools. The teachers have special training so they can teach young children water safety and how to swim.

Young children start in shallow water so that they can learn how to do simple things like putting their heads under water. Often this is at the shallow end of a pool, but even here some very small children may not be able to touch the bottom. If not, they can always hold on to the edge of the pool and learn how to kick their legs.

Most children learn how to swim after just a few lessons but often when they start they can only do a type of doggy paddle. It is most important that as they get older and stronger they should take some more lessons. In this way they will become good and strong swimmers and will also learn about how to behave sensibly in the water.

Learning to swim is important, but learning to swim well is just as important.

Re-read the report and answer the following questions.

1 When do many children learn to swim?

2 When are the special swimming classes held? Where are they sometimes held?

3 In what type of water do children often start learning to swim?

4 What do you need to do in order to become a good, strong swimmer?

5 Why are children taught to put their heads underwater?

6 Why is shallow water more suitable for new swimmers?

7 What do you think 'doggy paddle' is?

8 Who swims in the deep end?

9 Give at least one reason why it is important to learn how to swim.

10 List what you think are the differences between learning to swim and learning to swim really well.

11 What sort of training do you think is needed in order to teach swimming?

More things to do

List the things you need to do when you are learning to ride a skateboard. What would be the title of a report that contained this information?

How to find information in a book

An **explanation** helps the reader to understand **why** things are done or **how** they work. It begins with a **general statement** and then presents reasons.

Before you read

❀ How do you go about finding information in a book?

❀ Where would you find lots of books in a school?

Read this explanation.

HOW TO FIND INFORMATION IN A BOOK

Books often contain a lot of information. It can be a great help to us if we know how to find the information we need quickly.

All books have a title, which acts as the first clue. For example, if the title of a book is *Famous Steam Trains*, we know immediately that the book will have information on steam trains.

The title of a book and the name of the author are printed on the cover and on the title page.

Most books have a contents page. This lists all the different subjects covered in the book and the pages where this information can be found. So, in the example *Famous Steam Trains*, the contents page might look something like this:

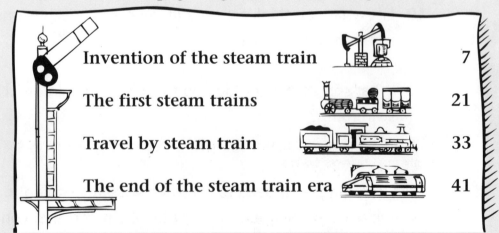

Notice that the contents page gives the page number where each section, or chapter, starts. So, if you wanted to find information about travelling by steam train, you would turn to page 33 and read that section. Some books also have an index at the back.

Re-read the explanation and answer the following questions.

1 Name two places where the title of the book is printed.

2 What does a contents page do?

3 Give the name of one section in the book *Famous Steam Trains*.

4 On what page would 'The end of the steam train era' begin?

5 What other name is often used for a section in a book?

6 Why might you need to be able to find information in a book quickly?

7 Do you think a contents page would be helpful for this? Why?

8 What information would you find on a title page?

9 Write these sentences in your notebook, marking them true or false.
All books have an index at the back.
Most books have a contents page.
The name of the author is always on the back cover.
You need to use the title page to find out where each chapter begins.
The book *Famous Steam Trains* has four chapters.

10 What might the following non-fiction books be about?
a *Mountains of Fire*
b *Top-scoring Strikers*
c *Caring for Creatures*

More things to do

Write a short booklet on a subject you find interesting. Divide the information into sections and create a contents page and a title page.

Things were better then

An **argument** presents a particular **view** about something and then gives **points** which support this view. It **sums up** at the end.

Before you read

❀ Do you think that life was better for boys and girls when Grandpa and Grandma were young? Give one reason for your view.

Read this argument.

THINGS WERE BETTER THEN

I think that boys and girls had a better life when Grandpa and Grandma were young.

First, cities and towns were not so crowded then. It would have been easier to get about and find space to play.

Second, the air was much cleaner than it is today. There were not so many cars, lorries, planes or factories causing pollution.

Our rivers and oceans were clean, too. There was not much rubbish, industrial waste or algae in them.

As there were very few cars, boys and girls could ride their bikes in safety. There was also less crime, which meant that parents didn't have to worry so much about their children being in danger.

Lastly, there was much more opportunity for boys and girls to spend time outdoors. Nowadays more and more trees are being cut down to build more and more houses, but then, even in the cities, there were more grassy areas with room for everyone to play.

All of these things make me think that life was better for boys and girls in my grandparents' day.

Re-read the argument and answer the following questions.

1 Were there more, or fewer, people living in cities in our grandparents' day?

2 In what way was the air different then?

3 Why was this?

4 Do boys and girls spend more, or less, time outdoors nowadays?

5 Why can't you ride your bike anywhere you wish today?

6 Find one sentence which sums up the argument.

7 How do cars, lorries, planes and factories cause pollution?

8 How do our rivers and oceans become polluted?

9 Arguments often use special words or phrases called technical terms. Write the meanings of the following three technical terms. Use your dictionary if you need help.

pollution

industrial waste

algae

10 Do you think life was better when Grandpa and Grandma were young? Why?

More things to do

Can you think of some reasons why life was not better when your grandparents were young? Write a short argument to support this view.

How to plant a tree

An **instruction** tells you how something is done. You have to know **what you need** and the **steps** you must follow.

Before you read

✿ If you have planted, or helped to plant, a tree at home or at school, write down two things you did which were very important. If you have not planted a tree, write down two things which you think might be important.

Read these instructions.

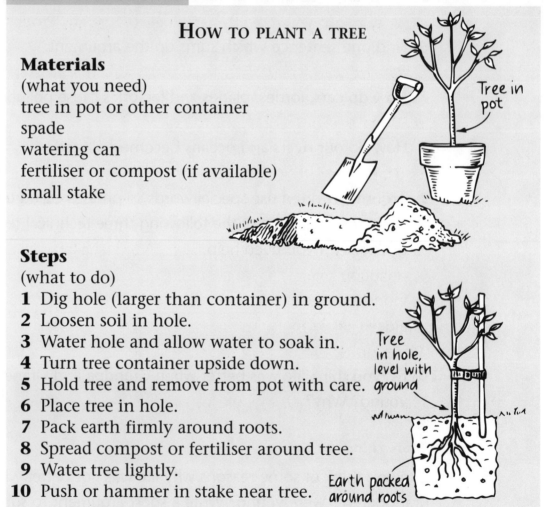

HOW TO PLANT A TREE

Materials
(what you need)
tree in pot or other container
spade
watering can
fertiliser or compost (if available)
small stake

Tree in pot

Steps
(what to do)
1 Dig hole (larger than container) in ground.
2 Loosen soil in hole.
3 Water hole and allow water to soak in.
4 Turn tree container upside down.
5 Hold tree and remove from pot with care.
6 Place tree in hole.
7 Pack earth firmly around roots.
8 Spread compost or fertiliser around tree.
9 Water tree lightly.
10 Push or hammer in stake near tree.

Tree in hole, level with ground

Earth packed around roots

Re-read the instructions and answer the following questions.

1 Name three things you need to plant a tree.

2 Name three things you do when you are planting a tree.

3 Why do you need water?

4 What is the spade used for?

5 Why would the hole need to be larger than the pot?

6 Why might you need to pack the earth tightly around the roots?

7 Do you know what a stake is? What would it be used for?

8 What are compost and fertiliser?

9 These instructions on how to plant a tree are laid out in steps. The steps are numbered 1 to 10. How does this help the reader?

10 The diagrams with the instructions are labelled. How do the labels help the reader?

More things to do

Plant, or help to plant, a tree.

Why might it be important to know how to plant a tree? Write as many reasons as you can in your notebook.

See the robbers passing by

Children sometimes use **rhymes** in the playground. These have both **rhyme** and **rhythm**.

Before you read

❖ Write down the name of any playground rhymes you and your friends hear or use when you're playing.

❖ What games do you use these rhymes for?

Read this playground rhyme.

SEE THE ROBBERS PASSING BY

See the robbers passing by,
Passing by, passing by,
See the robbers passing by,
My fair la-dy!

What's the robber done to you,
Done to you, done to you?
What's the robber done to you,
My fair la-dy?

Stole my watch and stole my chain,
Stole my chain, stole my chain,
Stole my watch and stole my chain,
My fair la-dy!

Off to prison you must go,
You must go, you must go,
Off to prison you must go,
My fair la-dy!

Traditional

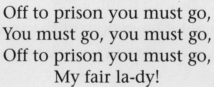

Re-read the playground rhyme and answer the following questions.

1 What did the robber steal?

2 What must happen to the robber?

3 Write out any words or phrases that show that this is an old rhyme.

4 The rhyme mentions stealing a watch and chain. Why would a watch have a chain?

5 What would have to happen to the robber before he was sent to prison?

6 Every verse has the same form. Write three more verses that begin with these lines:

He pinched my favourite trainers...
To the policeman you must go...
Stole my horse and stole my cart...

7 **a** In the past, what did a highwayman do?
b What was his form of transport?

8 What is another word for:
robber?
prison?

9 Prison is just one type of punishment. Do you think there might be better ways to punish robbers? What would these be?

More things to do

Make up a game that uses the playground rhyme 'See the robbers passing by'.

A letter to a school friend

A **recount** tells you about an **experience** that happened in the past. This letter is a recount. Look closely at how it is set out.

Before you read

❀ At what time of year do people go skiing?

❀ Give two reasons why a person who is on a skiing holiday might write to his or her school friends.

Read this letter.

Alphorn Chalet
Rue St Antoine
Beauville
Switzerland

19 January

Dear Abigail,

Disaster today – it is too windy to ski! Last night there was a blizzard, which is still raging. As I look through my window, all I can see is snow blowing everywhere. Everyone is staying indoors.

Up until yesterday the weather for skiing was perfect. Oliver and I have had skiing lessons every morning. Even Mum and Dad go to a ski class. The teachers are all very young and are great skiers. They show you what to do and then give you a chance to try. It looks easy but is often very hard work. My ski instructor says I am learning very quickly.

After our lesson we spend a couple of hours skiing down the slopes. Dad and Mum are good skiers, so they can do the hard runs. Oliver and I just ski down the gentle slopes. We find that's hard enough for us. We still fall over a lot!

Skiing makes you very hungry, so we always have a huge lunch when we get back to the chalet.

I hope this blizzard blows out today so we can ski again tomorrow. If it's fine, the snow will be great.

See you next week back at school.

Love Danielle.

Re-read Danielle's letter and answer the following questions.

1 Where was Danielle staying on her skiing holiday?

2 Who is on holiday with Danielle?

3 Why was Danielle writing to her friend, Abigail, today?

4 Where did Danielle normally eat lunch while she was on holiday?

5 Why did Danielle and Oliver take skiing lessons?

6 Why did Danielle's mother and father take skiing lessons if they were already good skiers?

7 Do you think Danielle was enjoying her holiday? What makes you think this?

8 What is a chalet?

9 What is a blizzard?

10 Name some countries in which people go skiing.

11 Imagine you were skiing down a snow-covered mountain. Write down three things that you might see.

More things to do

Here are three things that happened during the second week of Danielle's skiing holiday:

The family went cross-country skiing.

Oliver ran into another skier and bruised his hand.

The chair-lift broke down and Danielle had to wait for half an hour before she could get back on the ground.

Now write the second letter that Danielle sent to Abigail.

The genie

A **narrative** is a story that begins by telling the reader where and when things are happening. It continues with a series of events (**plot**), leading up to an event which changes the story. As a result, the plot can develop further or the story can come to an end.

Before you read

❀ What would you wish for if you were cold and had nowhere to go?

❀ If you found a magic genie, what would you ask for?

Read this story.

THE GENIE

It was a dark, dark night. The snow was coming down and it was very, very cold. The wind howled.

'Where will we sleep tonight?' asked Kirpal. 'If we stay out here in the snow we'll freeze to death.'

'We could try the train station,' said Scott. 'When it's very cold they sometimes let us stay there.'

They walked slowly towards the station. The wind was really cutting into them. They took a long time to get there. When they arrived they found all the lights were turned out and the station locked up. What could they do? They were so tired that they sat down on the steps.

Kirpal suddenly noticed a bottle lying on the ground nearby. It seemed to have a faint blue glow, so he bent over and picked it up. It was dirty, so he rubbed it on his trousers.

All at once there was a huge bang and flash and a magical figure in a glittering blue suit was standing next to them. Kirpal and Scott could not believe what they were seeing.

'Master, what do you desire? Tell me what I must do,' boomed the genie.

After a moment's hesitation, Kirpal whispered: 'Find us a warm place to stay for the night, please. And something hot to eat.'

In a blinding flash Kirpal and Scott found themselves in a room with two cosy beds. In the fireplace a fire was burning brightly. On the table were two plates of food that steamed deliciously.

The genie stood by the door waiting for the next command.

Re-read the story and answer the following questions.

1 What were the names of the two boys?

2 Was it summer or winter?

3 Where did the boys decide to go to look for shelter?

4 Why did Kirpal rub the bottle on his trousers?

5 What do you think the food on the table was like?

6 How do you think the two boys felt when the genie first appeared?

7 What is meant by 'the wind was really cutting into them'?

8 What do you think the genie looked like? Write a short description of him.

9 How did the boys feel once they had been transported to the room by the genie?

10 If you could have any wish, what would you choose?

More things to do

Write down what you think Kirpal's next command to the genie will be.

Why there is lightning then thunder

An **explanation** makes clear **how** things work or **why** things happen. It opens with an **overall statement** followed by points which explain how or why.

Before you read

❀ When you see lightning, what do you usually hear?

Read this explanation.

WHY THERE IS LIGHTNING THEN THUNDER

Thunderstorms are the more common type of storm. They happen when warm, damp air rises and then forms clouds as it cools. Thunderclouds are huge and black, and they stretch very high into the sky. The currents of air inside the cloud cause heavy rain, thunder and lightning.

Lightning is really a giant electric spark, which is often several kilometres long. Thunder is the noise made when the lightning causes the air to heat up and expand suddenly. When this explodes we hear the sound we call thunder.

A lightning flash, and the clap of thunder that comes from it, happen at about the same time. We see the lightning first and hear the sound later because light travels very quickly and we see it almost immediately. Sound travels much more slowly and so takes longer to reach our ears. If the lightning is several kilometres away this may take a number of seconds.

One way to tell if a flash of lightning is a long way off is to count the seconds until you hear the thunder. If you count one second, then the lightning and thunder are about three kilometres off. If the flash and the thunder seem to happen together, you will know that the lightning is very close. Watch out!

Re-read the explanation and answer the following questions.

1 What is lightning?

2 What causes thunder?

3 Which travels faster – light or sound?

4 How can you check if a flash of lightning is a long way off?

5 Why would you have to 'watch out' if the flash of lightning and the sound of the thunder seemed to occur together?

6 Why is it not dangerous if you hear thunder long after you see the flash of lightning?

7 What should you do if you are caught out in a storm to be safe from lightning?

8 Thunderstorms are just one kind of storm. Can you think of any others?

9 Write these sentences in your notebook, marking them true or false.
Lightning and thunder never occur simultaneously.
If you count five seconds in between thunder and lightning, the storm is about 15 kilometres away.
Thunder is the sound of warm air colliding with cool air.

More things to do

Write an explanation of the way a fish breathes. Use the following facts and give your writing the heading 'How a fish breathes'.
Fish, like us, need oxygen to breathe. Fish suck in water through their mouths. Their gills take the oxygen from the water. We take it from the air; they take it from the water. The oxygen goes into their blood. The waste water is passed out through their gills.

Argument

Travel teaches you many things

An **argument** begins with the author stating a **point of view**. This is followed by **reasons** that support that point of view. At the end the author sums up the argument to reach a **conclusion**.

Before you read

❀ Have you ever travelled? Where did you go? Who did you travel with? Why did you travel?

❀ What was the most important thing you learned while you were travelling?

Read through this argument.

TRAVEL TEACHES YOU MANY THINGS

When you travel you are able to learn many things that you cannot learn at school or at home.

By travelling to other countries you can find out about the people who live there. If you are able to spend time in the place where they live you will get a real opportunity to understand many things about the lives of people in other places.

You can see what kind of lifestyles they have – what their homes are like, what they eat, what kind of clothes they wear. You can learn what types of jobs they do, how they get about and how they spend their leisure time. By walking among them, sitting near them in restaurants and buses and hearing the language they speak, you will really start to know them in a way you would never be able to from books, films or television programmes.

You can also learn a lot about yourself. How different is your lifestyle, your language, the food you eat? Could you live like them, eat the food they eat, learn their language? When you start to ask yourself these things, you will learn a great deal about others, and a lot about yourself.

Travel teaches you about other people and other places. It also encourages you to think about yourself and where you live. Many of the things you experience by spending time in another country cannot be learned in any other way.

Re-read the argument and answer the following questions.

1 Write out the statements that you think are correct.

Travel takes you to where people live.

Travel teaches you about others and yourself.

Travel costs too much so it's not worth it.

You can learn just as much from seeing a programme on TV.

Travel would help nations to understand each other better.

There are too many health risks when you are travelling.

2 List three things that you may notice are different if you travel to another country or area.

3 Why is it important to ask questions when you travel?

4 What does 'lifestyle' mean?

5 Do you think you would learn more about yourself, or about other people, if you went travelling?

6 Copy one sentence that you think is the most important idea from this argument.

7 How does the writer sum up this argument?

8 Is 'Travel teaches you many things' a good title for this argument? Can you think of a different title that would be suitable?

9 Write down any reasons you can think of that do not support this writer's argument.

More things to do

Where would you like to go for a holiday? Write an argument, telling the reader why you think you should go there.

A narrow escape

An **adventure story** is a type of **narrative**. At the start we are introduced to the characters and find out what the adventure will be. This introduction is followed by exciting happenings and an ending in which everything is worked out.

Before you read

❀ Think of some places where an adventure story called *A Narrow Escape* might take place. Write down two of them.

Read this story.

A NARROW ESCAPE

Lucy heard the order above the boom of the cascading water: 'Paddles in. Lean left.'

She obeyed, as if by instinct, and the rubber raft surged down the rapid, through the gap in the rocks, and moved swiftly into calmer, safer water. Another crisis was over.

Lucy had not expected to be on this wild journey. She and her Dad had planned to hike through the rainforest, taking their time, walking at a relaxed pace. But the rains had come early this year. There was news of a flood coming down from the mountains. The paths would soon be under water and the river a raging torrent. They had to get out. Fast. And by raft.

'Are you OK, Lucy?'

That was her father.

'Paddle hard, left. Now!'

That was the instructor.

Lucy paddled furiously, hardly drawing breath. She tried to feel brave by remembering that the instructor knew the river like the back of his hand.

'The toughest stretch is round the next bend, crew!' he yelled. 'Do exactly as I say and we'll make it all right. Lucy, sit right next to me and hang on tight to the rope. Good luck everyone!'

The raft started to gather speed. Lucy could see the frothy rapids ahead. She was scared, really scared. Crash! The raft bounced off the rocky wall of the cliff on the right. Thump! It landed hard, after plunging down a steep cascade of water. Still the little crew clung on and the raft rushed forward, swept faster and faster and faster by the surging water. Just when she thought that the nightmare would go on forever she heard the instructor shout, 'One more drop, crew, a big one, and then we're through.'

The raft's nose turned downwards and plunged over the waterfall. It hit the bottom hard and nearly turned over. Lucy's grip on the rope loosened; almost as if in slow motion she felt herself tip; and then she was in the raging water!

There was silence all around her, the silence of the deep. Her lungs wanted air, but she knew she had to hold her breath. Up, up through the bubbles she went. And then, just as her lungs felt like they were about to burst, she broke the surface and gasped air, beautiful air.

Then she felt something grab her life-jacket and lift her, dripping, out of the water. It was the strong arm of the instructor.

'Got you, young tadpole,' he said, as he pulled Lucy on board. Welcome to the club, the Tadpole Club. Only rafters who fall over the side are allowed to join. It's very exclusive.'

Lucy saw her father's grey, worried face and smiled at him. 'I'm OK, Dad,' she gasped. 'I'm just a very wet tadpole.'

Re-read the story and answer the following questions.

1 Where did the adventure take place?

2 Who was the experienced rafter?

3 What was the raft made of?

4 Why do you think the instructor asked Lucy to come and sit by him?

5 Why did Lucy's father look grey and worried?

6 a How did a rafter become a member of the Tadpole Club?
b Why do you think the club was called the Tadpole Club?

7 What is the crisis (the most tense and exciting moment) in this story?

More things to do

Write an alternative ending in which the instructor is unable to grab Lucy's life-jacket. What do you think happens?

Hare in summer

Some **poems** have animals as their subject. This poem, written by the Australian poet Flexmore Hudson, is about a hare.

Before you read

✿ Have you ever seen a hare? What other animal is it like?

✿ Imagine it is a hot day in summer, you are walking in the countryside and you see a hare. What would you expect the hare to be doing?

Read this poem.

HARE IN SUMMER

In the little strips of shade
that a strainer-post has made,
squats a weakly panting hare.
All day he has squatted there.
Only with the shade he shifts.
As I approach, he slowly lifts
his goggling eyes, but will not run,
fearing me less than the naked sun.

Flexmore Hudson

Re-read the poem and answer the following questions.

1 What season of the year is it?

2 The hare is sitting in the shade. What is making the shade?

3 When does the hare change its position?

4 What happens when the poet approaches the hare?

5 What words tell you the hare is very hot?

6 Which of these three things is the hare most frightened of? Write the answer in your notebook.
someone approaching
not having enough to eat
going out of the shade and into the very hot sun

7 Why does the hare 'slowly lift his goggling eyes'?

8 Why has the hare just 'squatted there'?

9 Why does the poet describe the sun as 'naked sun'?

10 What do you think a 'strainer-post' is?

11 What would happen to you if you were caught outside in the very hot sun and could find no shade?

12 What words in the poem rhyme with:
hare?
run?
shade?
shifts?

More things to do

Do some research to find out more about hares and where and how they live.
Draw a picture of a hare keeping out of the sun by sitting in the shade of a large rock.

The haunted house

This piece of **drama** has been written as a **radio play**. When you listen to a radio play you must use your imagination because you cannot see what is happening. **Sound effects** are important, and the characters' voices must be very expressive.

Before you read

❀ What sounds might you hear in a haunted house?

Read this radio play.

THE HAUNTED HOUSE

Night sounds – the hoot of an owl, the croak of a frog, the howl of a dog in the distance. Footsteps are heard. Two girls are approaching an old house.

JOANNE *(in a shaking voice):* I'm scared, Tanya. Let's go home.

TANYA *(in a much firmer voice):* Don't be a wimp, Joanne. You're still not worrying about ghosts, are you? There are no such things as ghosts. Here's the place. Let me switch the torch on. *(A click is heard.)* Does the light make you feel better?

JOANNE *(still shaky and uncertain):* But we should be at your house. My Mum will be really mad if she knows we're here.

TANYA: Oh for goodness sake, stop fussing! Our houses are only over the road. We can soon run back. It's an adventure.

JOANNE: I don't like adventures. This place has been empty for years. It could be dangerous, and I've heard people say that it's haunted.

(More night sounds are heard and the moaning of the wind.)

TANYA: Look! The back door's open. Let's go in.

(There is a creaking sound as the door is opened wider, then the shuffling sound of the girls' footsteps as they go inside.)

JOANNE *(in a whisper):* It's spooky in here, Tanya. So dark and quiet. Where are you? Can I hold your hand?

TANYA *(in a louder, firmer whisper):* There's nothing in here to be scared of. Nothing at all, apart from an old couch. No ghosts. Nothing.

(A spooky, rustling sound is heard – crumpled paper can be used.)

JOANNE *(terrified):* Listen to that noise! What is it? It's coming from the other room. It must be the ghost!

TANYA *(now frightened too):* And it's coming closer! Quick – behind the couch!

(A thump and a bump are heard as the girls dive behind the couch.)

TANYA: I'll turn off the torch. *(A click is heard.)* Lie still!

JOANNE *(in a panic):* It's the ghost. I know it is. It's coming to get us!

(The rustling sound becomes louder. The girls scream.)

TANYA: I've got to see what it is. *(A click is heard as the torch is turned on, then a pause, then the meow of a lonely cat.)*

JOANNE *(relieved):* Look Tanya – it's a cat! Only a cat.

TANYA *(in a very firm voice):* There's your ghost, Joanne. A poor hungry cat. Let's take it home.

(The cat meows again.)

TANYA: Come on, Ghostie. We'll give you some milk.

(The cat begins to purr. Night sounds are heard again, but softer and less threatening in the background.)

TANYA *(patting the cat):* Nice Ghostie.

Re-read the play and answer the following questions.

1 At what time of day do you think the play took place?

2 What did the girls do when they heard the ghostly sound?

3 Which girl was braver? Give your reasons.

4 a Why do the girls go into the haunted house?
  b Would you have gone into the haunted house?

5 Why are the sound effects very important in this play?

6 This play has a surprise ending. What is it?

7 What words tell you that the girls were frightened?

More things to do

Read this radio play for your group or class. Include sound effects.
Make up your own play about a spooky happening.